VIOLIN SCALES

FOR BEGINNING JAZZ VIOLIN

HARRY HUNT, JR., MFA

Violin Scales for Beginning Jazz Violin
Harry Hunt, Jr., MFA

Published by Harry Hunt, Jr.
Chicago, IL
harryhuntjr.com

ISBN: 978-1-954127-15-9 (paperback)

Printed in the USA
First Edition

DEDICATION

Harry Simpson Hunt, Sr. was a noted Chicago jazz musician. As a gifted artist and teacher, he played all the instruments; however, the trumpet was his instrument of choice. His unique approach to playing was unprecedented as he tapped into and unlocked the talents of many upcoming, inspiring musicians. Everyone who knew him unanimously agreed that he breathed and ate music. Harry's brilliance as an instructor, along with the music he produced, will forever be appreciated by generations to come.

ABOUT THE AUTHOR

As an accomplished violinist, media composer, and educator, Harry Hunt, Jr. is known as one of the more creative contemporary violinists in the music industry. He began training in his youth as a classical violinist, but his curiosity led him to explore modern genres and styles of music.

During college, Harry studied jazz guitar and piano, which led him to a Bachelor's degree in jazz guitar studies. After college, he applied what he learned from the guitar and piano to the violin, creating his own unique, soulful style and sound. Now, his mission is to help violinists explore other types of music by sharing the experiences and methods that helped him to become the modern violinist that he is today.

Harry has toured internationally and performed and recorded with several renowned artists, including Chance the Rapper, Tony! Toni! Tone!, Chaka Khan, and Carl Thomas.

CONTENTS

PLAY-ALONG PRACTICE TRACKS

To Stream or Download

Click or Visit

harryhuntjr.net/book-vsfbjv

OTHER LINKS

Stream from Bandcamp

https://vsfbjv.bandcamp.com/releases

Download from Dropbox

https://www.dropbox.com/sh/sy5d8mwvphhr7y6/AAAOgdgGcSpETQ8J5nk3UjfDa?dl=0

(bookmark links in your browser for quicker access)

INTRODUCTION

This book gives an introduction to five popular scales in jazz. Scales are one of many steps towards learning jazz improvisation. Scales are the alphabet of jazz. Learning and memorizing jazz scales will help you create the 'sentences' and 'phrases' you need to improvise with.

Below is a short description of the five scales covered in this book.

Major Pentatonic Scales

The major pentatonic scale is a five-note scale.

The major pentatonic scale comes from scale degrees 1-2-3-5-6 of the major scale.

It works on major or major 7th chords.

Blues Scales

The blues scale is a six-note scale.

The blues scales comes from scale degrees 1-b3-4-b5-5-b7 of the natural minor scale.

It works on minor or dominant chords.

Dorian Scales

Dorian is a seven-note scale from the 2nd mode of the major scale.

It comes from raising the 6th scale degree up a half-step of the natural minor scale.

Dorian works on minor 7th chords.

Mixolydian Scales

Mixolydian is a seven-note scale from the 5th mode of the major scale.

It comes from lowering the 7th scale degree down a half-step of the major scale.

Mixolydian works on dominant 7th chords.

Bebop Scales

The bebop scale is an eight-note scale.

It comes from adding a b7 scale degree to a major scale

The bebop scale works on dominant 7th chords.

C MAJOR PENTATONIC SCALE

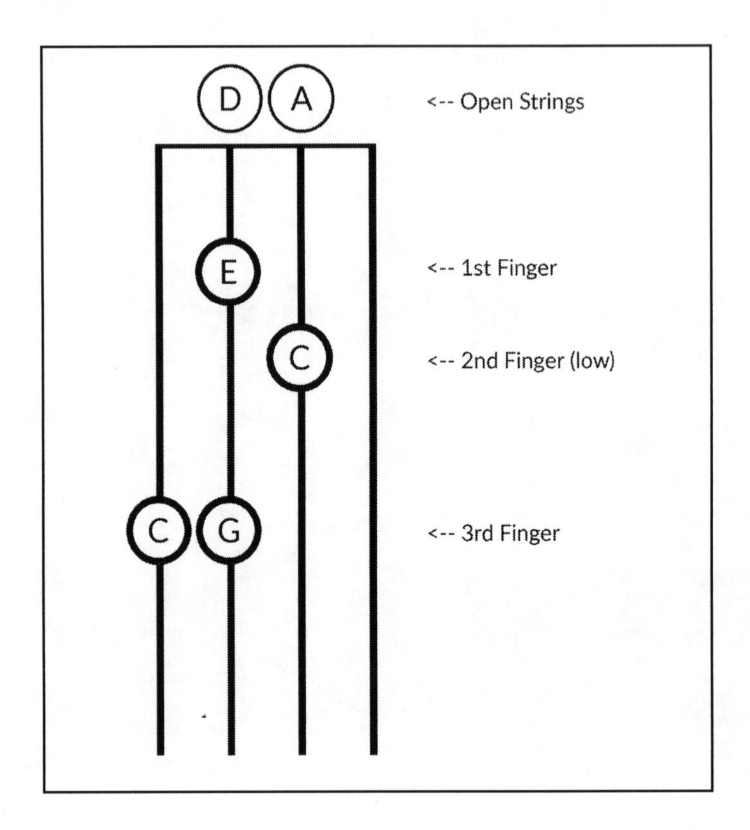

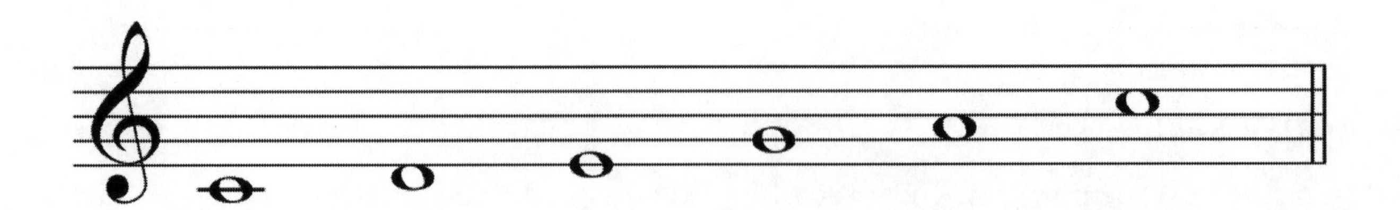

Chords most commonly used on:

C, C6, Cmaj7, Fmaj7

1

2
3
4

G MAJOR PENTATONIC SCALE

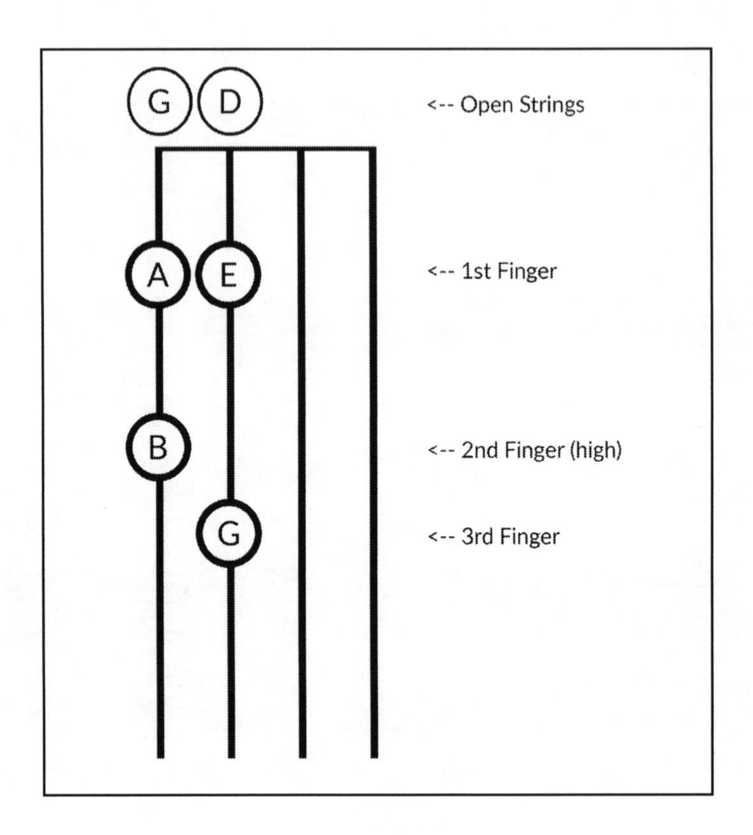

Chords most commonly used on:

G, G6, Gmaj7, Cmaj7

1

2
3
4

F MAJOR PENTATONIC SCALE

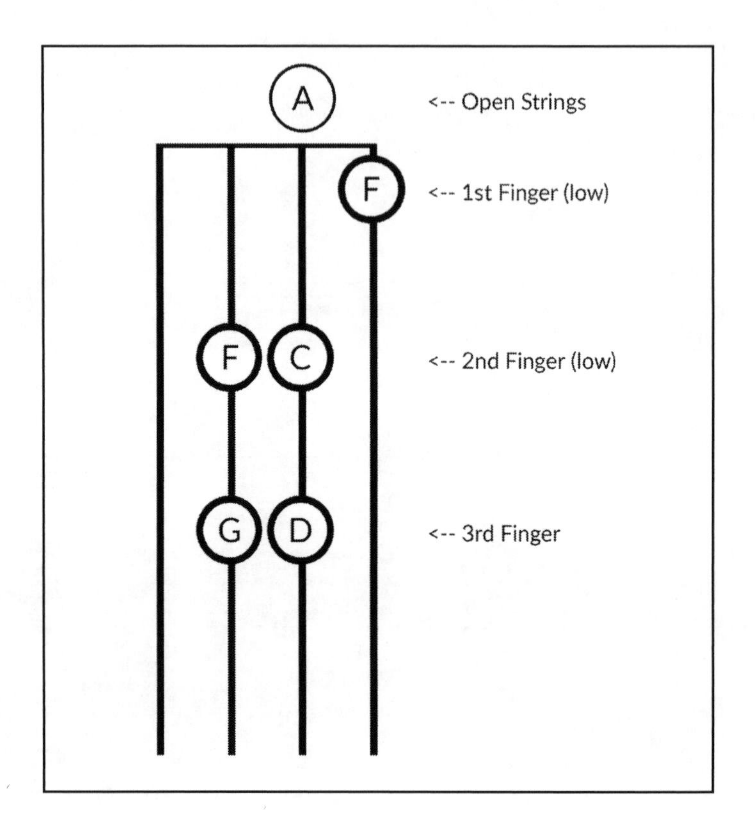

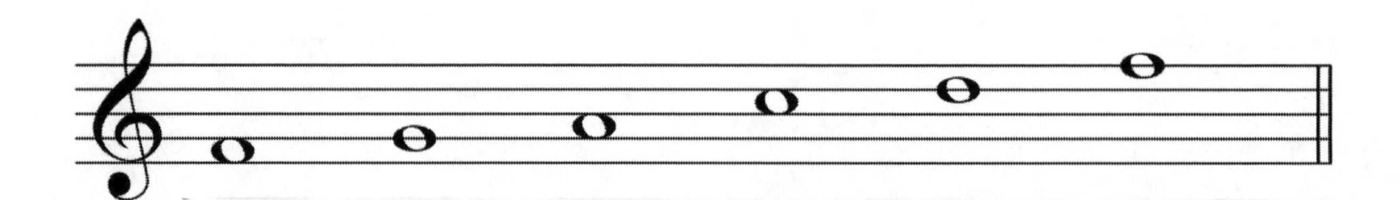

Chords most commonly used on:

F, F⁶, Fmaj7, Bbmaj7

1

2
3
4

D MAJOR PENTATONIC SCALE

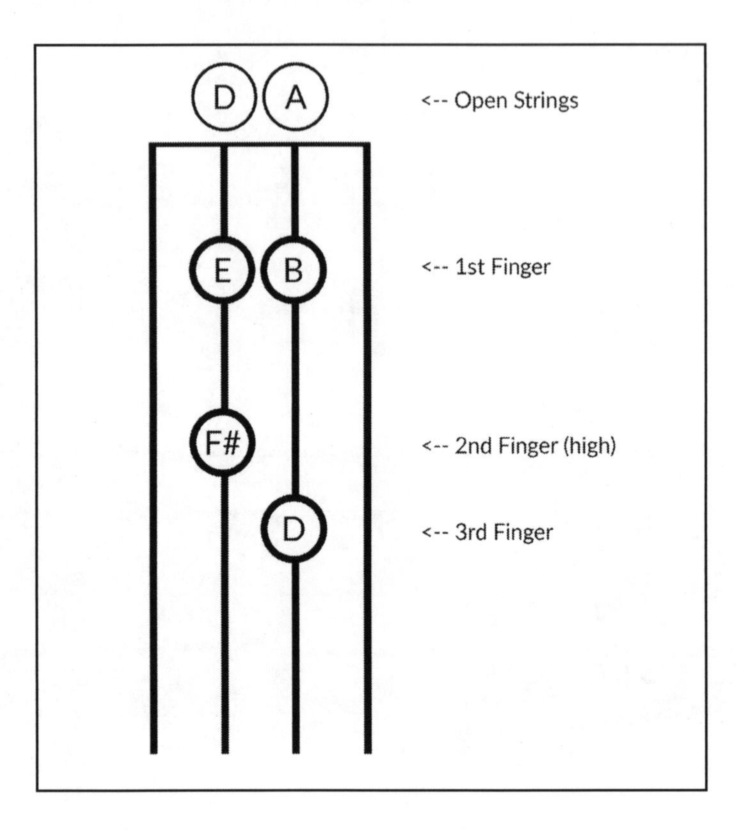

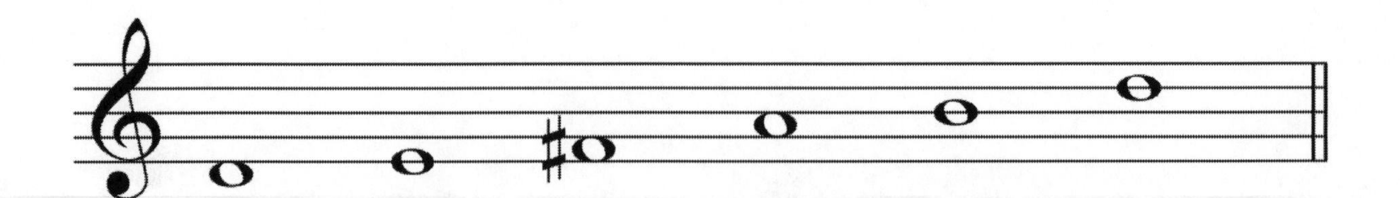

Chords most commonly used on:

D, D6, Dmaj7, Gmaj7

1

2
3
4

A MINOR BLUES SCALE

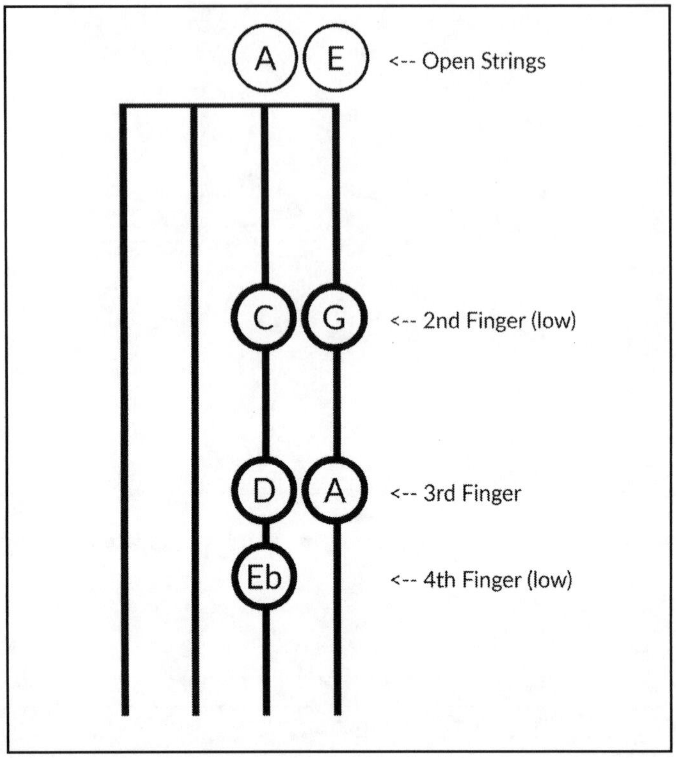

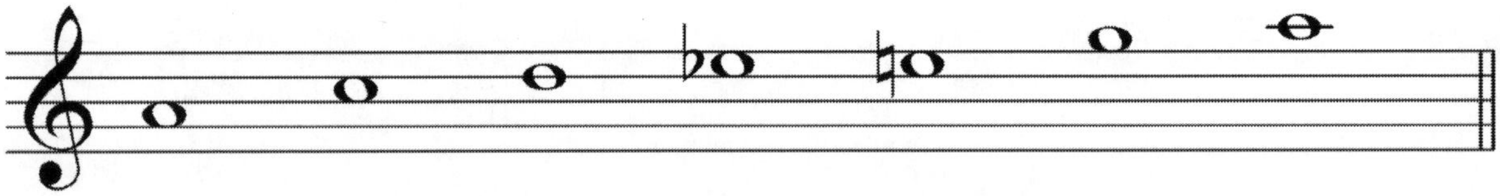

Chords most commonly used on:

A^{m7}, A⁷

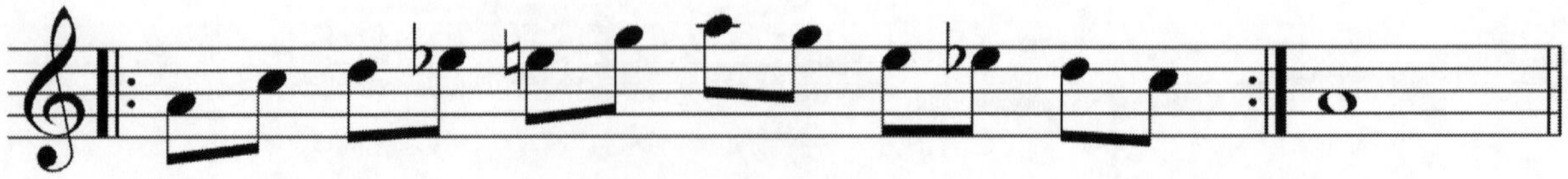

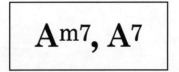

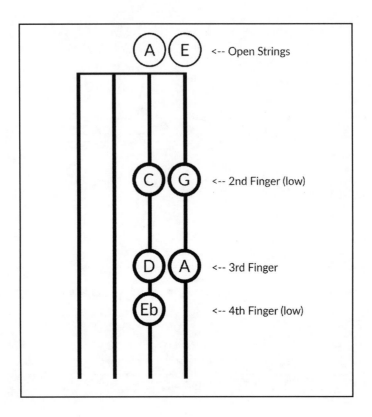

D MINOR BLUES SCALE

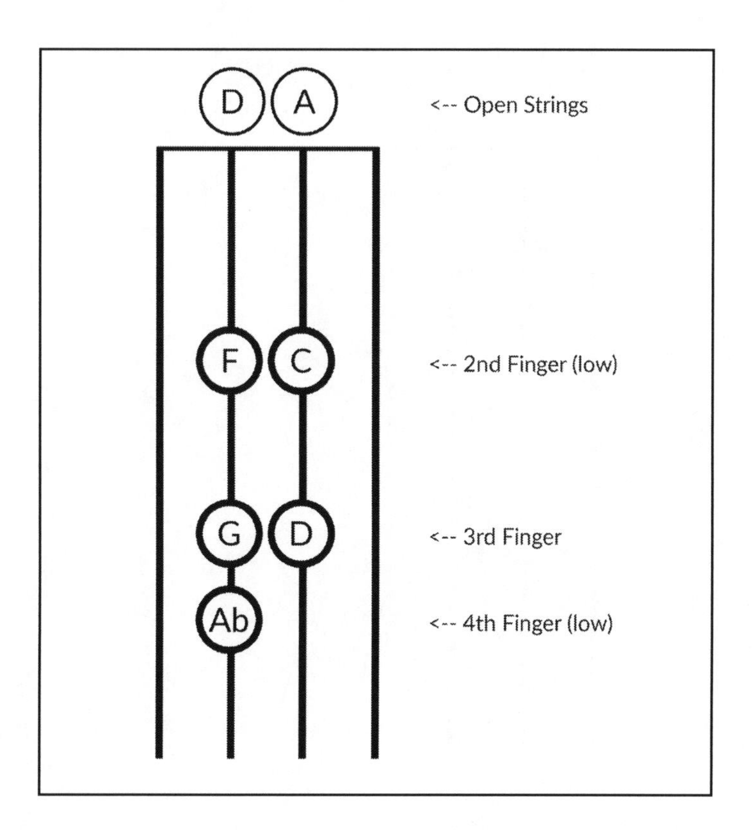

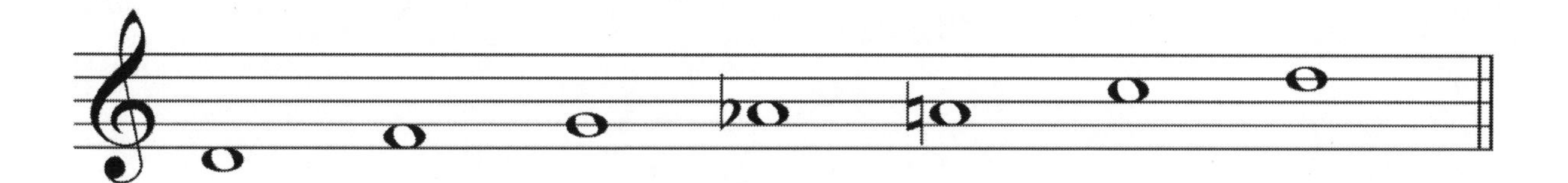

Chords most commonly used on:

Dm7, D7

E MINOR BLUES SCALE

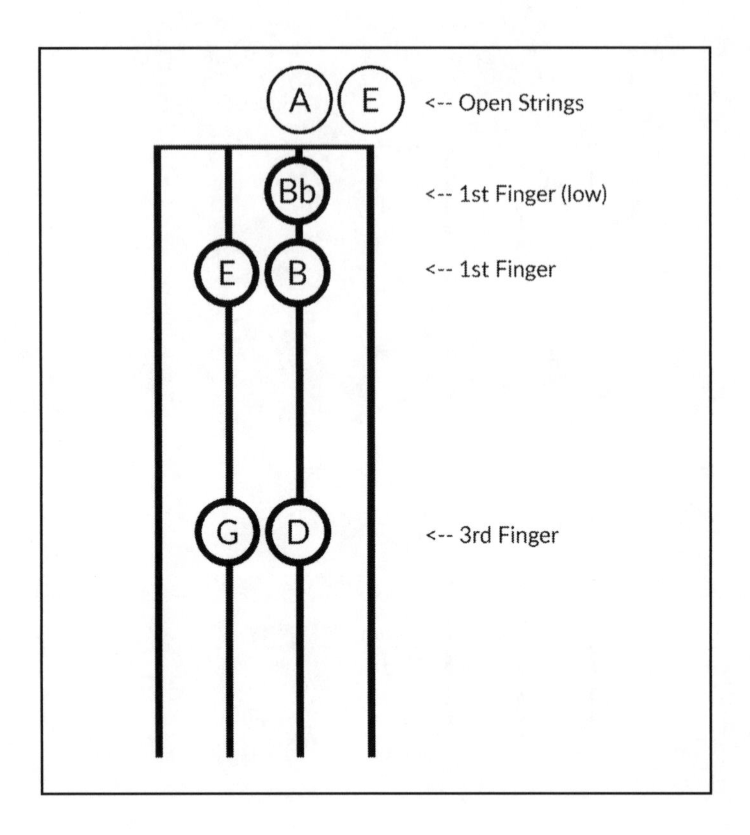

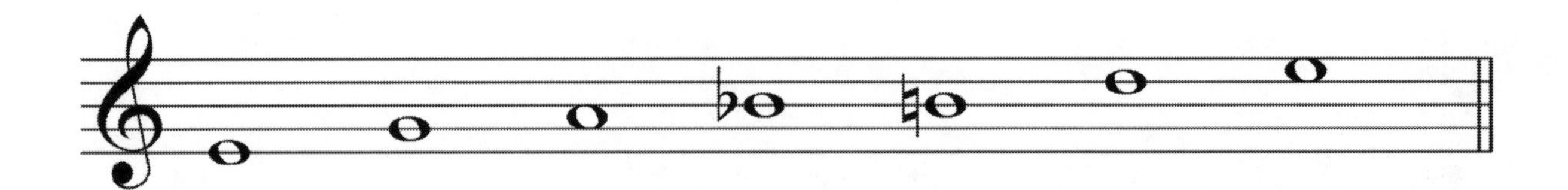

Chords most commonly used on:

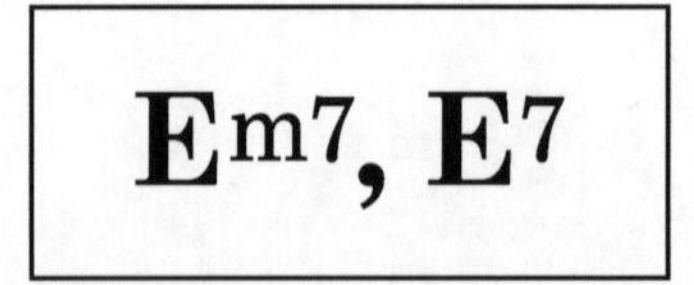

B MINOR BLUES SCALE

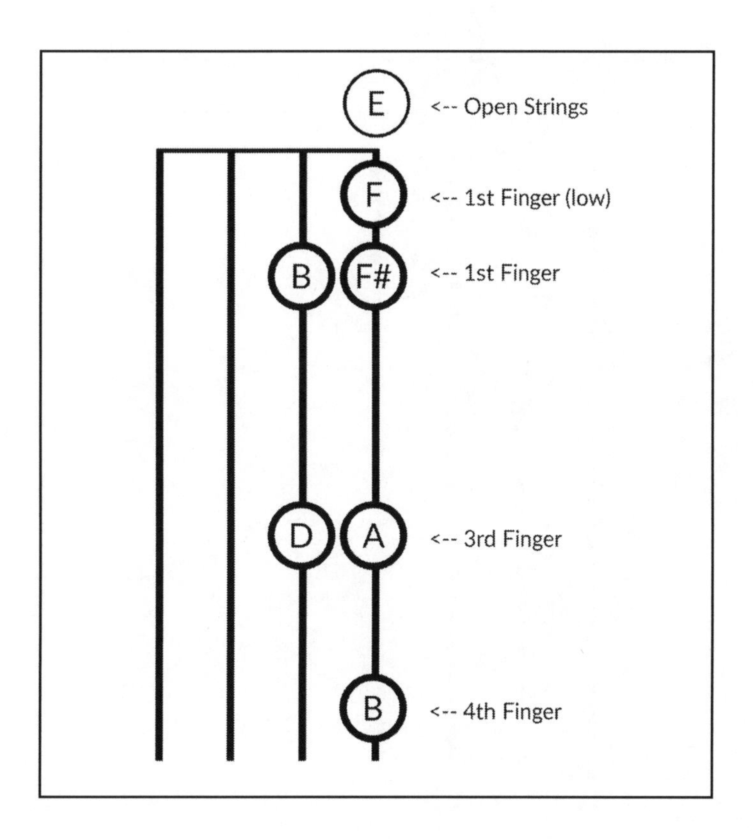

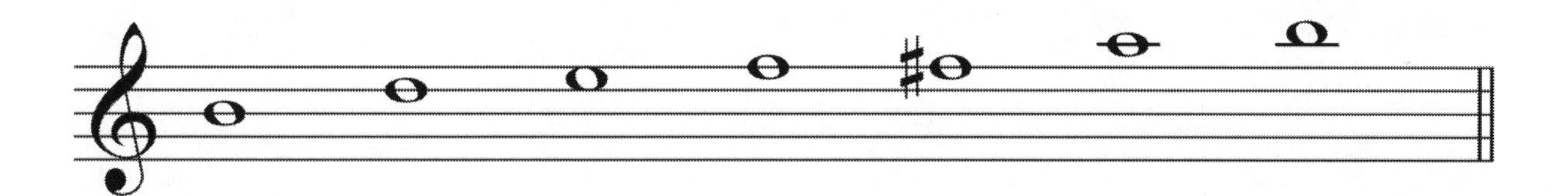

Chords most commonly used on:

B^{m7}, B^{7}

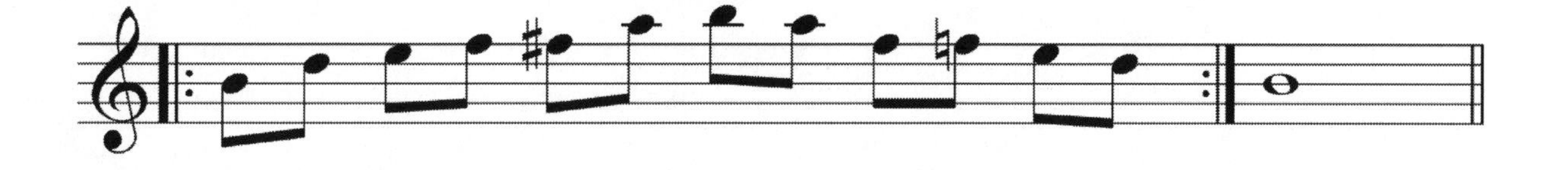

D DORIAN MINOR SCALE

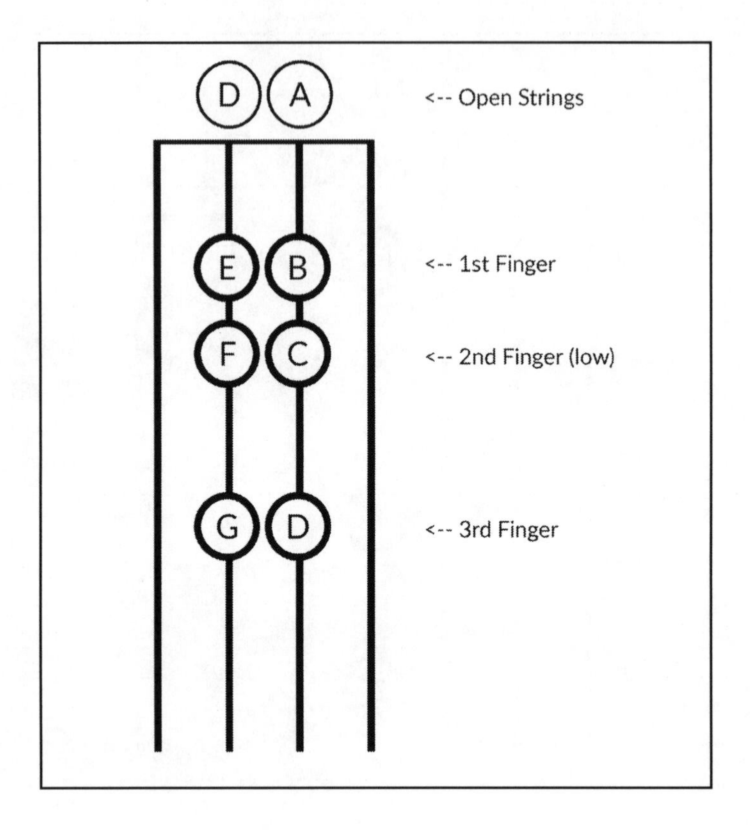

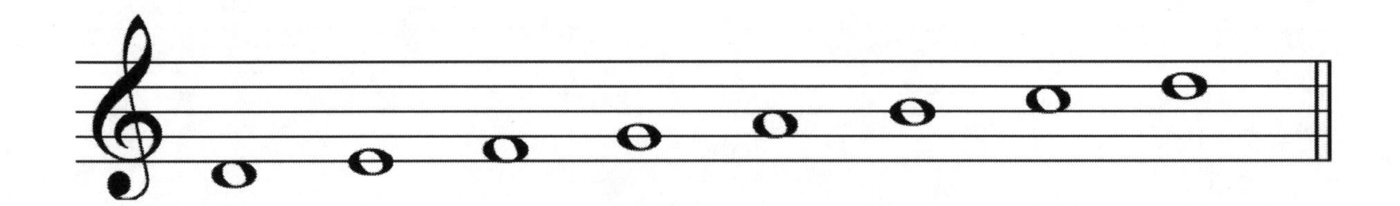

D Dorian is the 2nd mode of C Major.

It is most commonly used on a D Minor Seventh Chord:

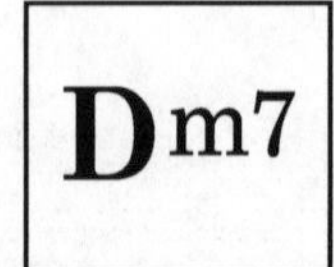

©2021 Harry Hunt, Jr.

A DORIAN MINOR SCALE

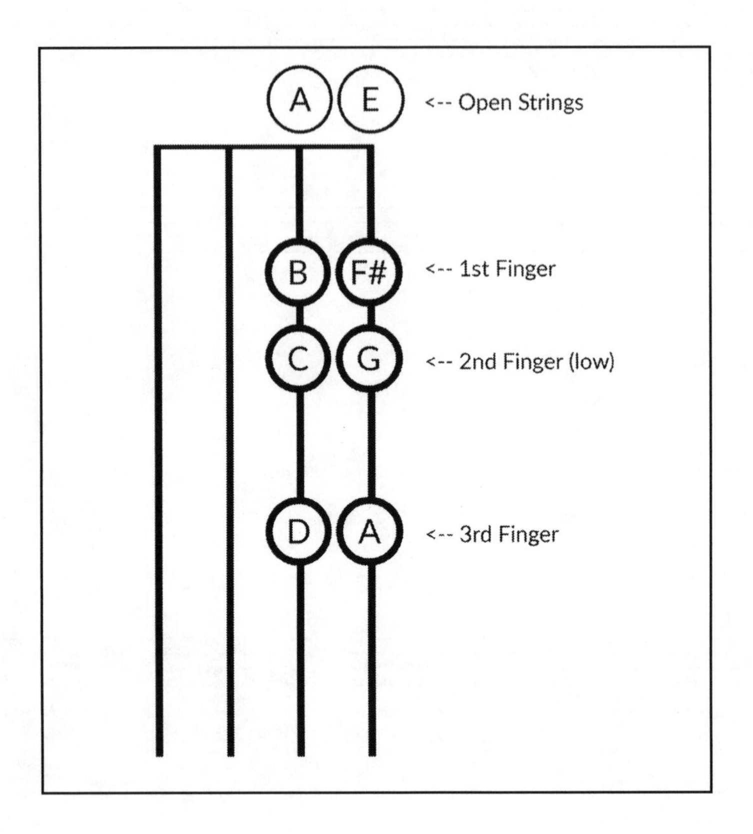

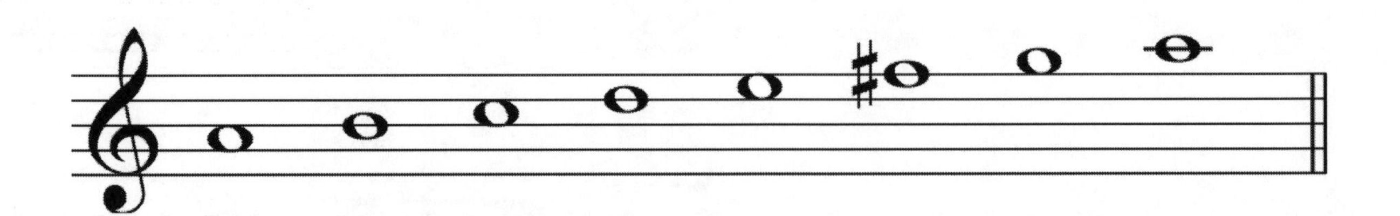

A Dorian is the 2nd mode of G Major.

It is most commonly used on an A Minor Seventh Chord:

Am7

1
0 1 2 3 0 1 2 3
2
3
4

G DORIAN MINOR SCALE

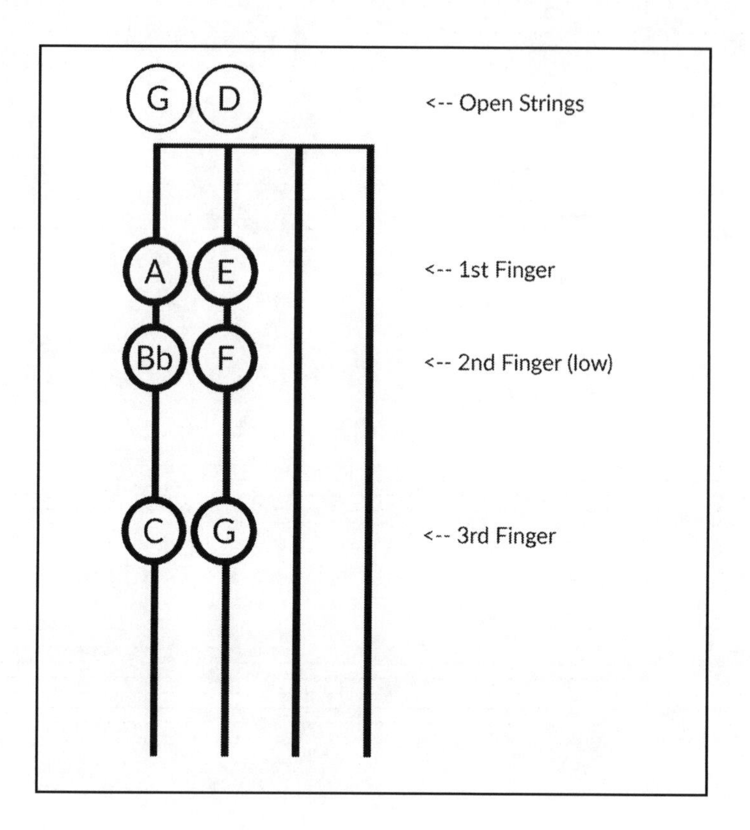

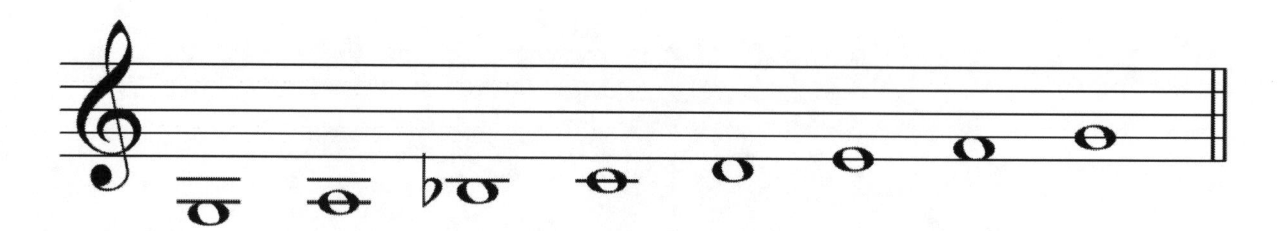

G Dorian is the 2nd mode of F Major.

It is most commonly used on a G Minor Seventh Chord:

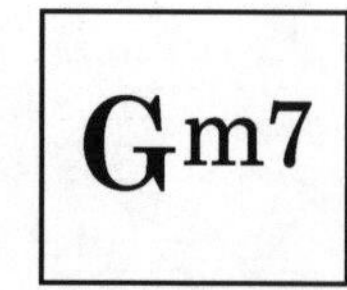

1
0
1
2
3
0
1
2
3
2
3
4

E DORIAN MINOR SCALE

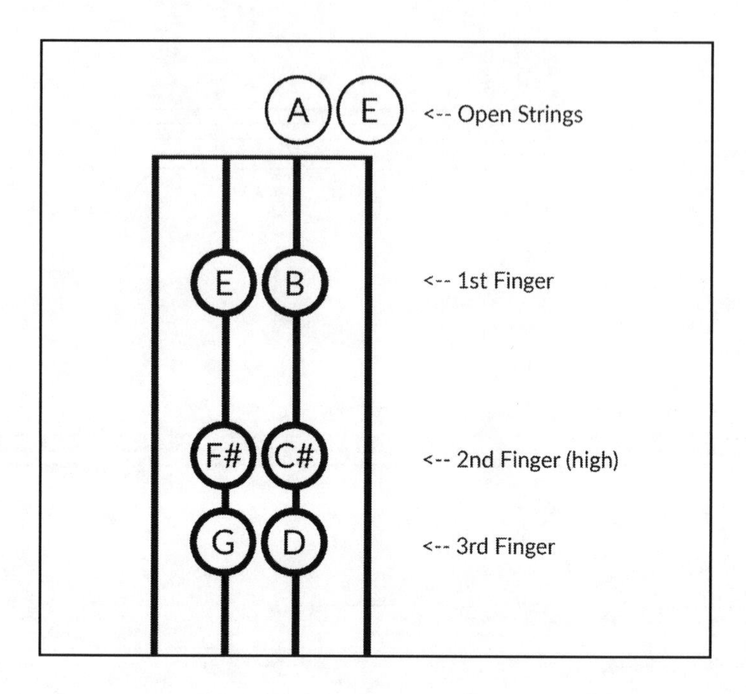

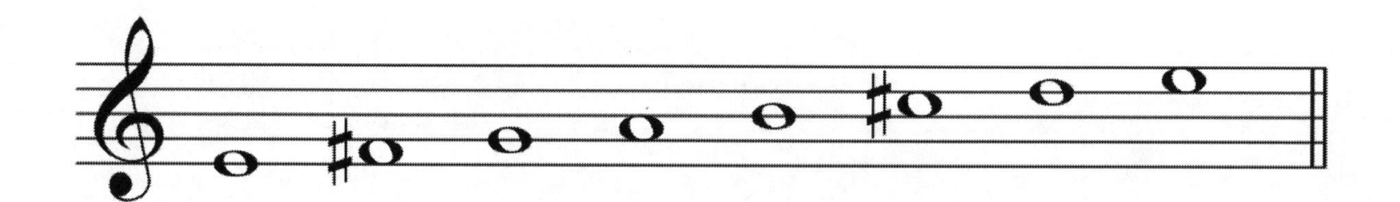

E Dorian is the 2nd mode of D Major.

It is most commonly used on an E Minor Seventh Chord:

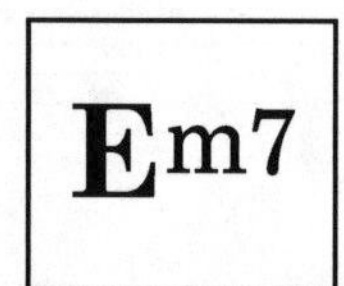

1
1 2 3 0 1 2 3 4
0
2
3
4

G MIXOLYDIAN SCALE

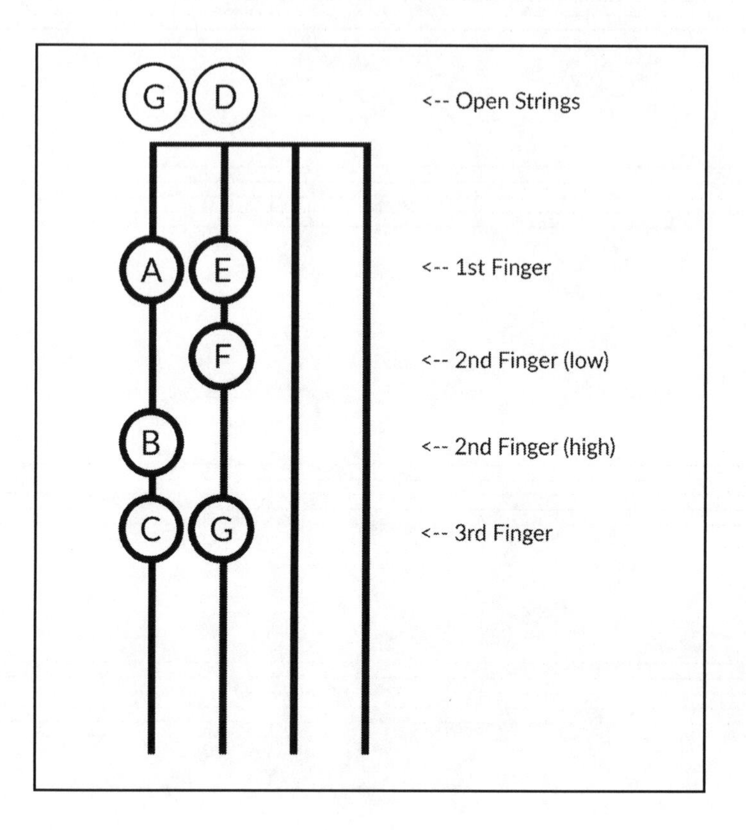

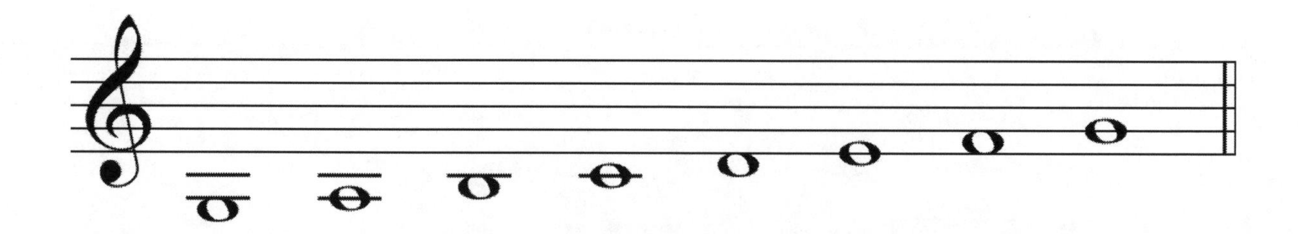

G Mixolydian is the 5th mode of C Major.

It is most commonly used on a G Dominant Seventh Chord:

G7

0 1 2 3 0 1 2 3
1
2
3
4

D MIXOLYDIAN SCALE

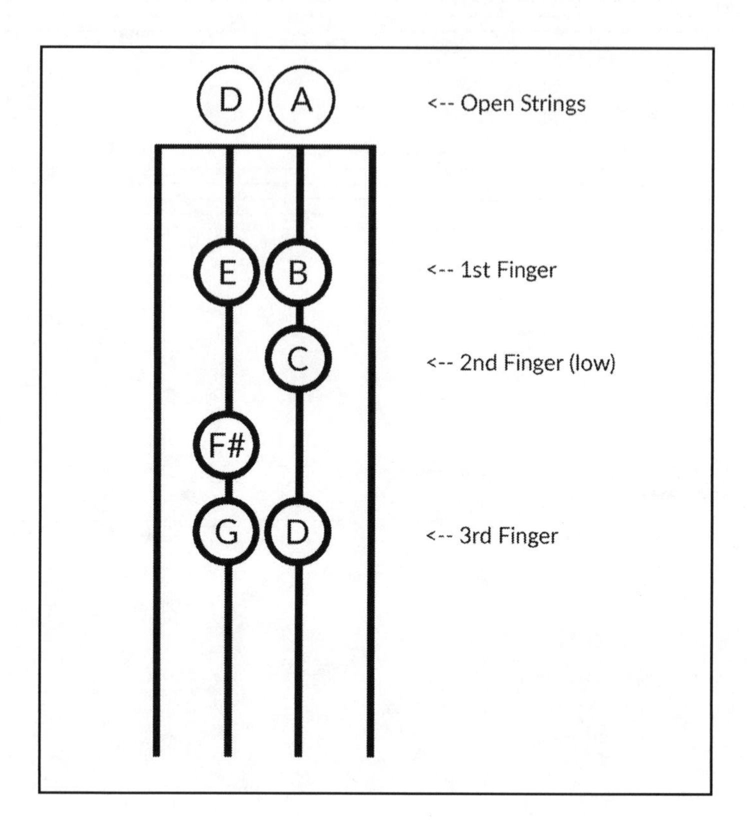

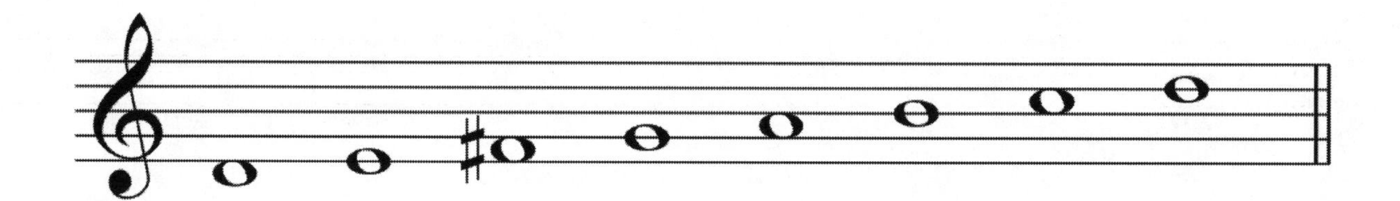

D Mixolydian is the 5th mode of G Major.

It is most commonly used on a D Dominant Seventh Chord:

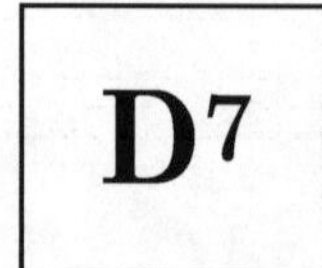

1
0
1
2
3
0
1
2
3
2
3
4

C MIXOLYDIAN SCALE

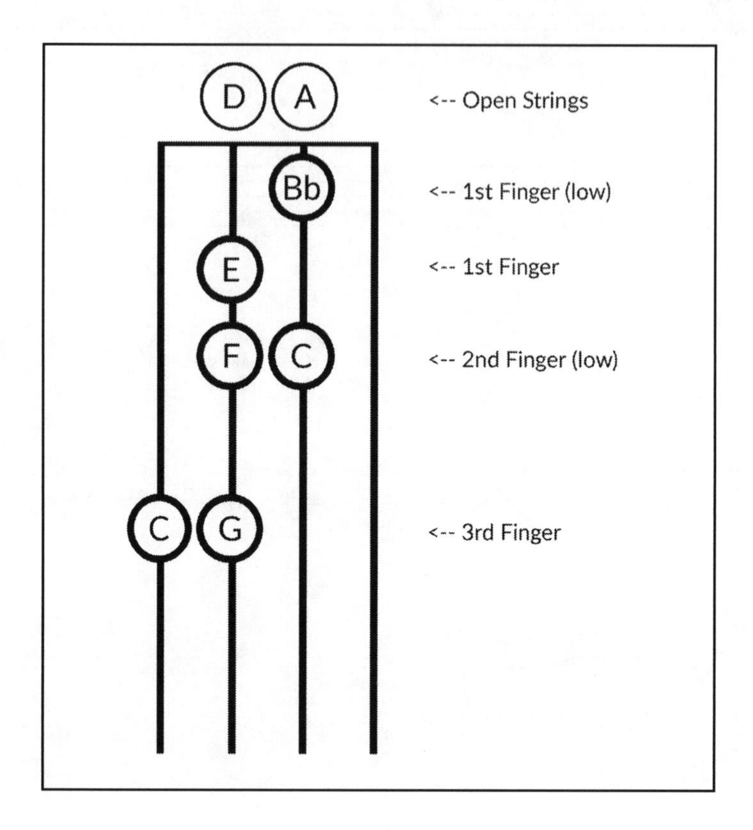

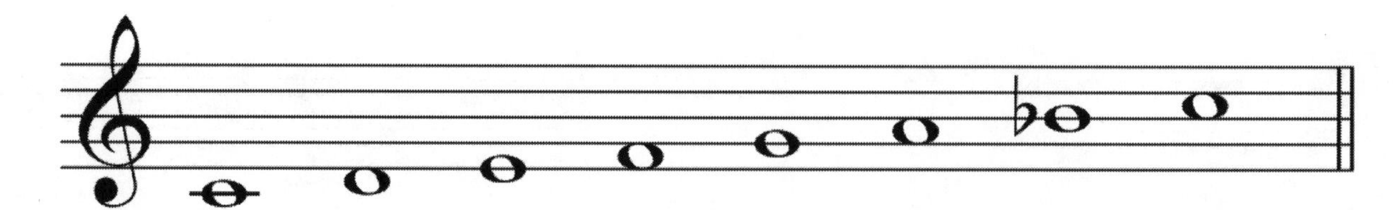

C Mixolydian is the 5th mode of F Major.

It is most commonly used on a C Dominant Seventh Chord:

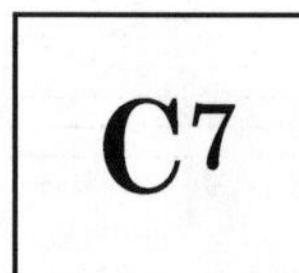

1
3 0 1 2 3 0 1 2
2
3
4

A MIXOLYDIAN SCALE

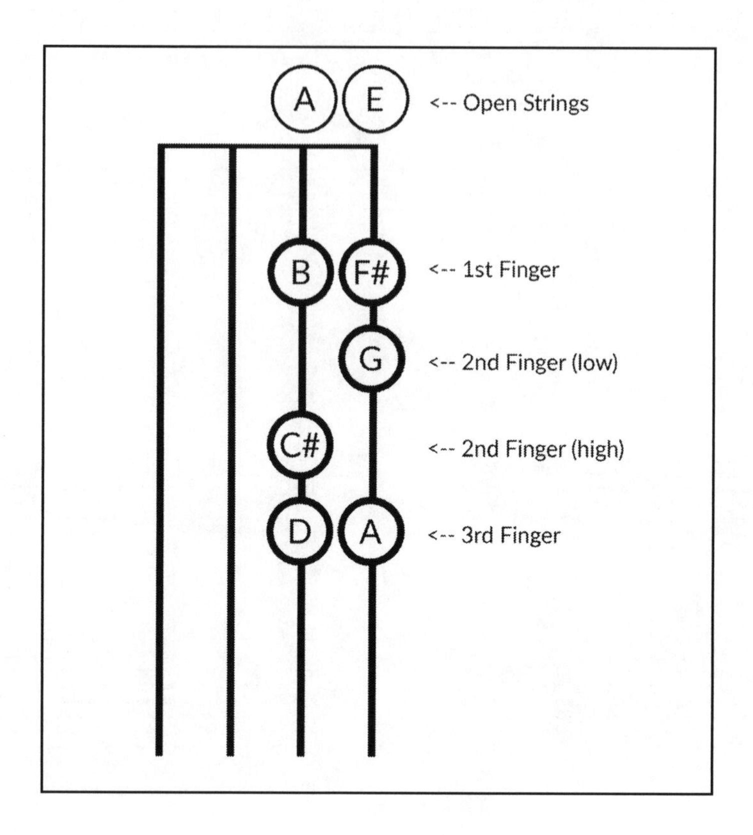

A Mixolydian is the 5th mode of D Major.

It is most commonly used on an A Dominant Seventh Chord:

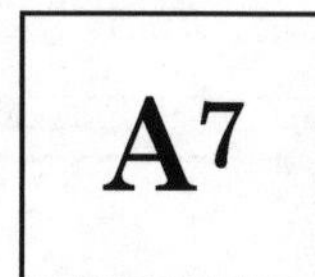

1
0
1
2
3
0
1
2
3
2
3
4

G BEBOP SCALE

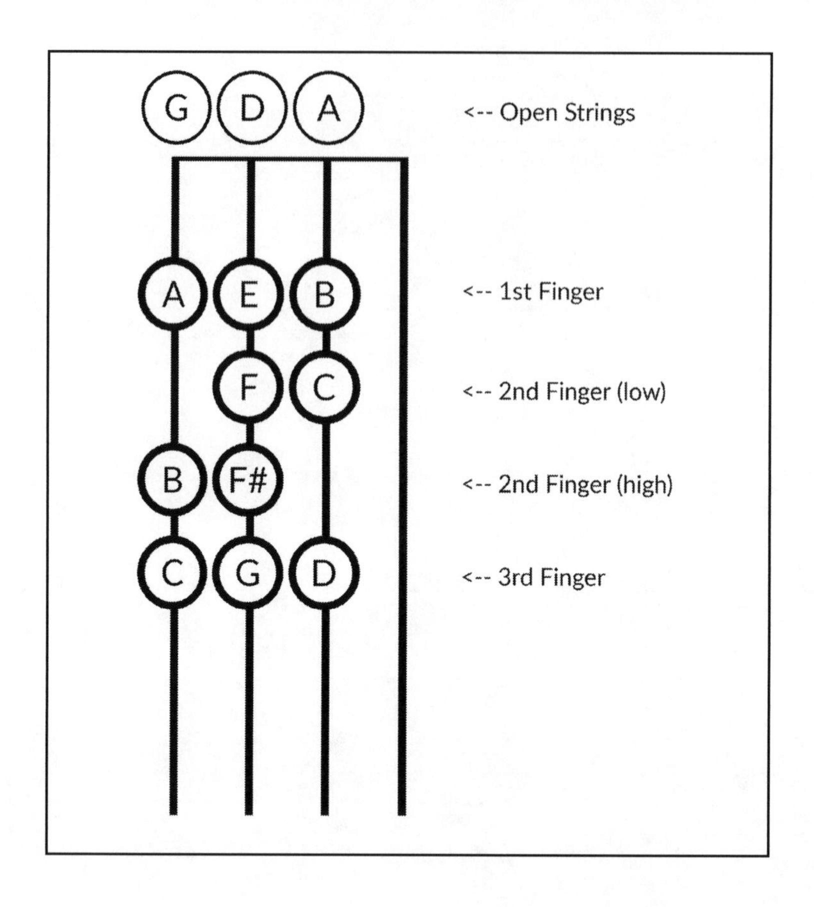

Chords most commonly used on:

G7

C BEBOP SCALE

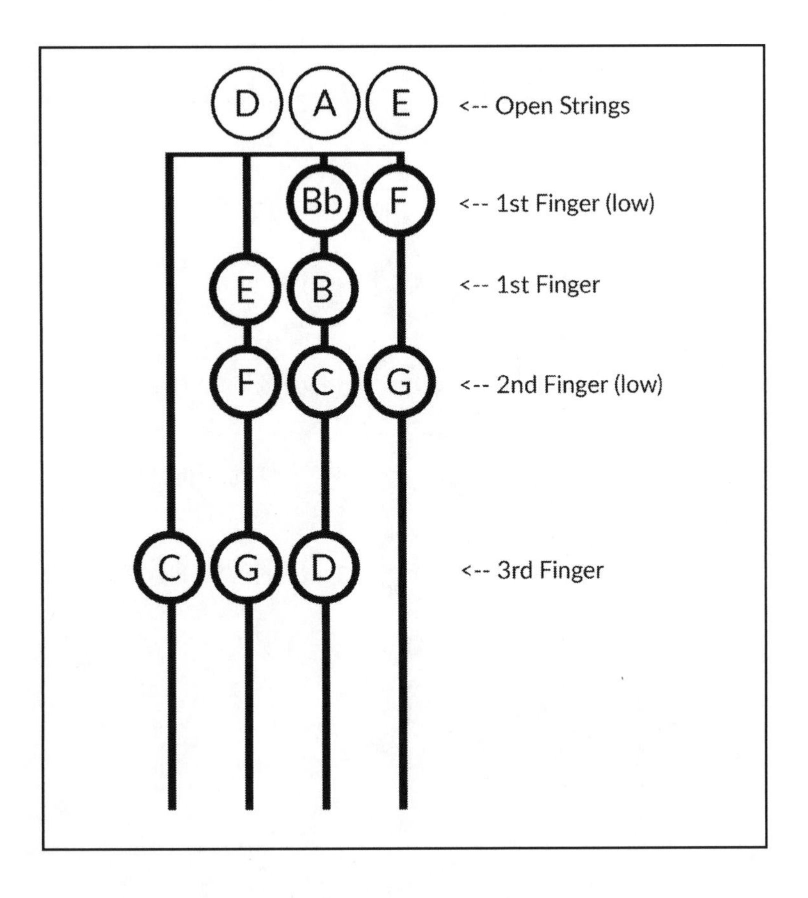

Chords most commonly used on:

C7

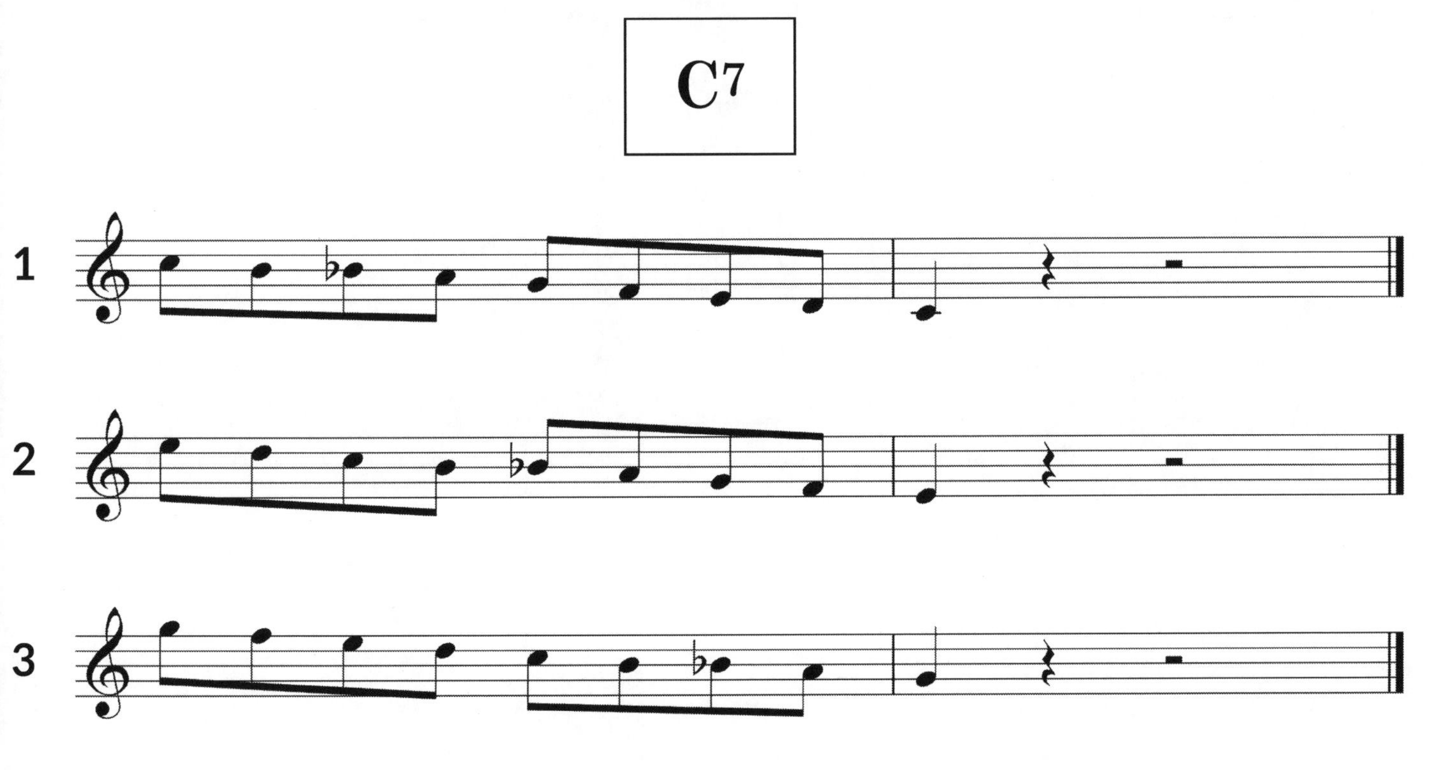

D BEBOP SCALE

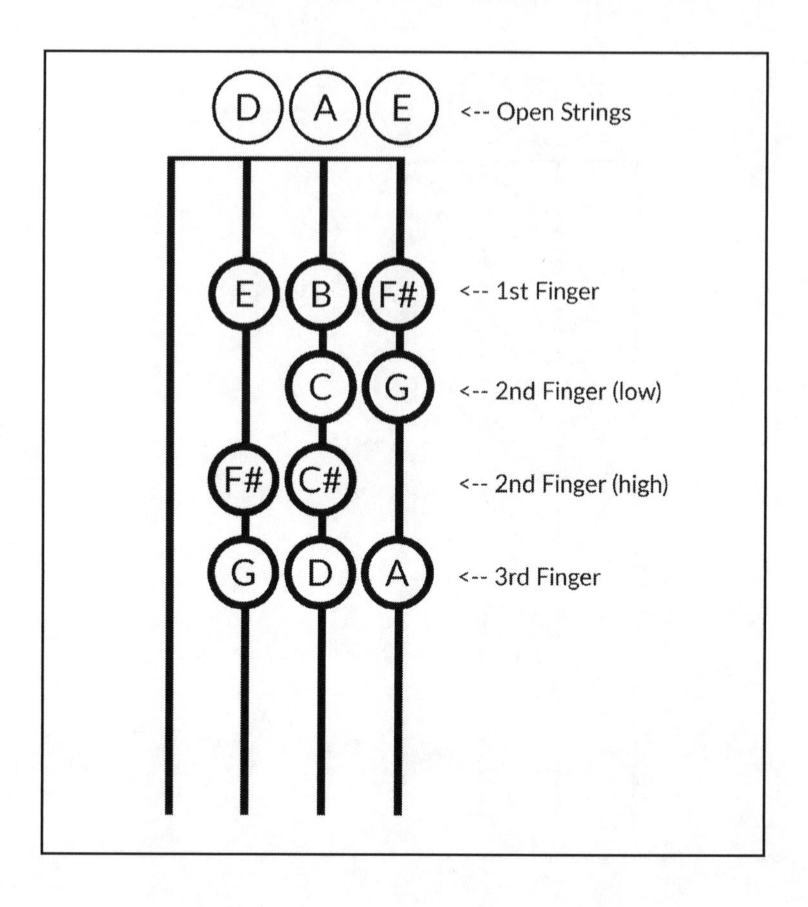

Chords most commonly used on:

D7

A BEBOP SCALE

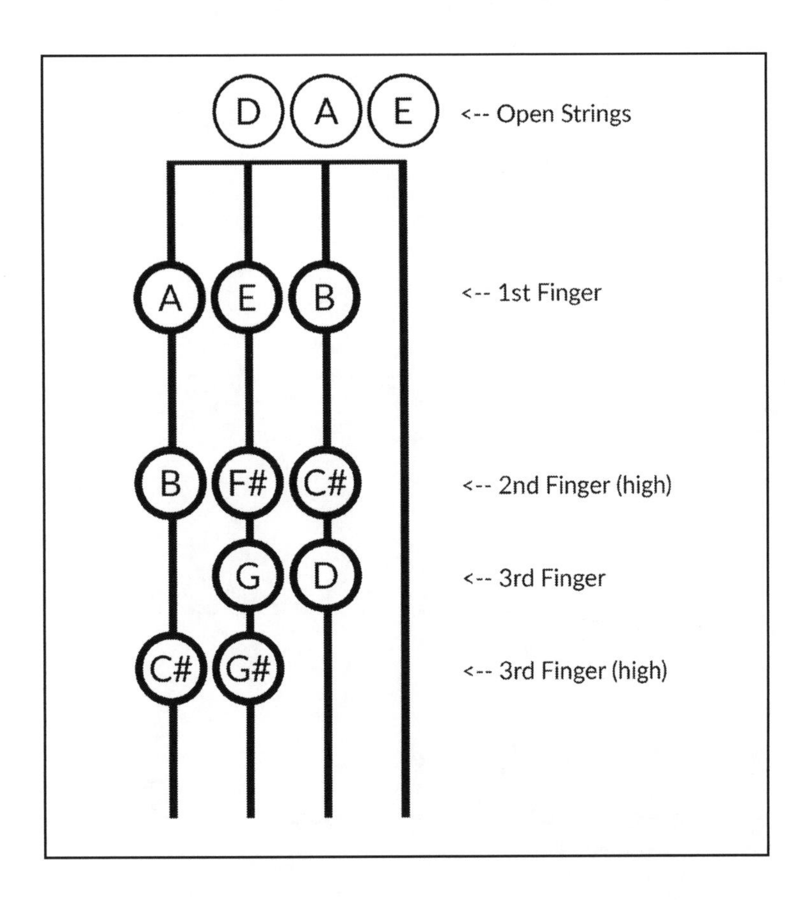

Chords most commonly used on:

A7

BOOKS ALSO AVAILABLE

CLASSICAL HITS FOR JAZZ VIOLINISTS

Play your favorite classical melodies along with jazz play-along backing tracks.

Classical Melodies for Jazz Violin does not require any improvisation. You can just have fun, read the melodies and play along with the jazz audio track.

BOOKS ALSO AVAILABLE

24 EASY CLASSICAL VIOLIN SOLOS: BOOK 1

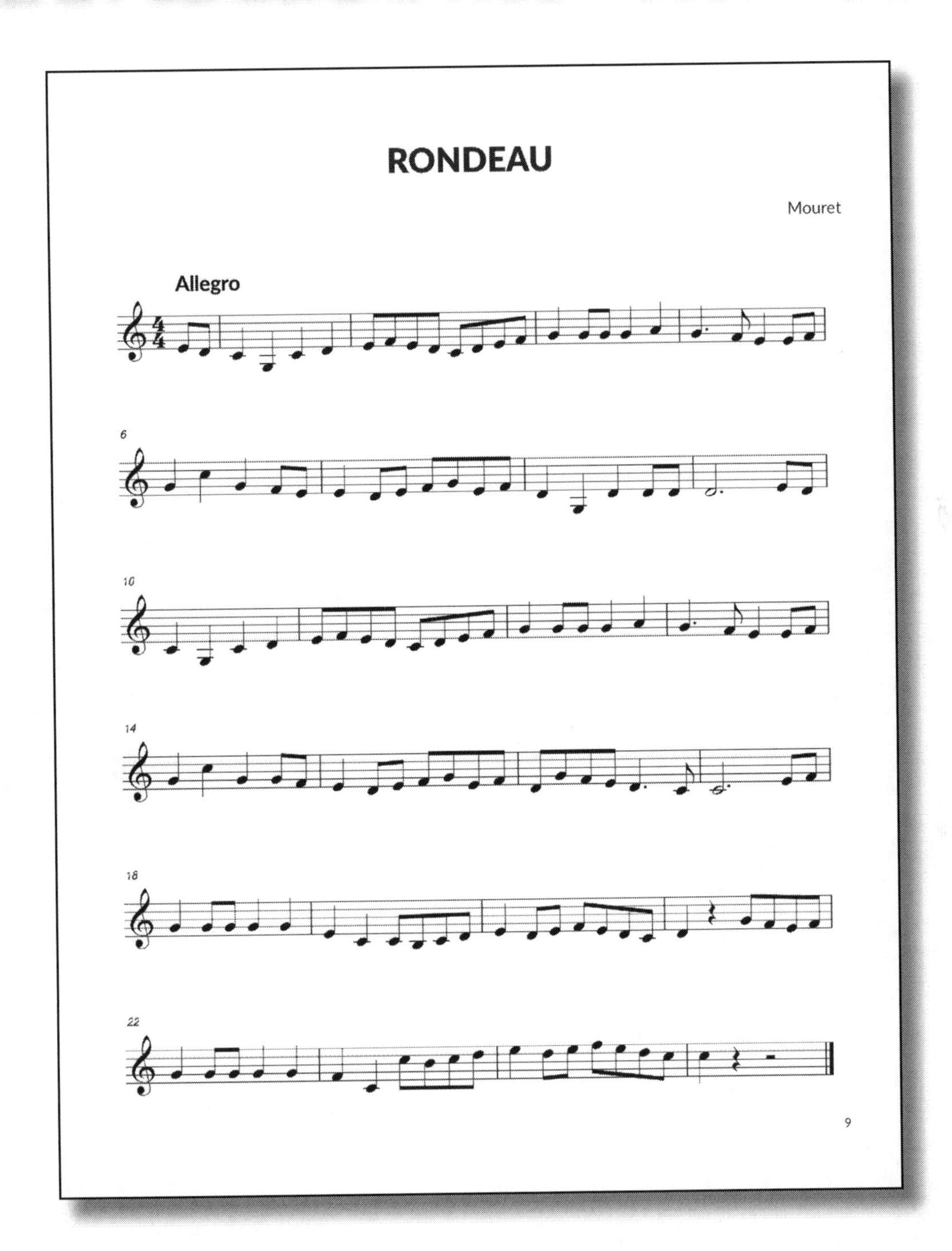

24 Easy Classical Violin Solos has short and simple pieces of some of your favorite classical melodies.

The music comes from classical composers such as: *Bach, Mozart, Beethoven, Haydn, Handel, Brahms and more.*

harryhuntjr.com/violin-bookstore

Made in United States
Troutdale, OR
03/29/2024

18804899R00024